This Big Town Bumper Book belongs to

The Big Town Bumper Book

British Library Cataloguing in Publication Data
A catalogue record of this book is available from the British Library.
ISBN 0340879149

Brum programmes, Character and Logo
© 1989-2002 Ragdoll Limited
Brum wordmark and Logo are trademarks of Ragdoll Limited
© 2004 Ragdoll Limited
Words and music for 'Brum, Brum, gets things done'
© 2001 Artemis. Music and composers Beggs/Harris/Sheppard

First edition published 2004
10 9 8 7 6 5 4 3 2 1

Published by Hodder Children's Books
a division of Hodder Headline Limited
338 Euston Road, London, NW1 3BH

Originated by Dot Gradations Ltd, UK
Printed in China

The Big Town Bumper Book

Hodder
Children's
Books

A division of Hodder Headline Limited

Contents

Save the goodies ● Time to save the day! ● Way to go Brum! ● Brum's a superhero! ● Catch the baddies

The Big Town baddies are in town and taking things. Their stolen loot is hidden in your bumper book. Can you find these stolen objects?

Who's in Town?

The Visiting Man has lost his photo album. Quick as a flash, superhero Brum finds it in the Square.

Wow! It's Brum's friends.

She loves stunt bikes.

It's Lucky the kitten.

Cool slippers!

He lost a statue.

Granny Slippers

They work in the Big Town.

Bob and Job

He lost a runaway ball.

Two Big Town baddies.

Their clothes never fit.

This was pinched from a washing line.

So was this.

Bubble and Squeak

His best gnome.

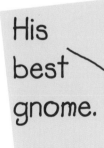

Gnorman is six.

Silly stripy jumper!

Thanks to Brum you've got the picture. So let's go with Brum into the Big Town!

Mr Brillo

It was a big day in the Big Town.
All over the Square, big flags were fluttering.
Bob and Job had been very busy.

Brum whizzed around the tall flagpoles, and came across a jumble of small flags.

The two Big Town workers were in a tangle. Brum *whirled* his wheels and *twirled* his handle.

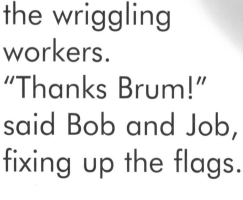

Brum soon unwrapped the wriggling workers.
"Thanks Brum!" said Bob and Job, fixing up the flags.

It was time to move the statue of the Mayoress. Bob tied a rope onto the trolley and tugged. But the stone statue wouldn't budge.

Brum tooted... and **scooted** to the statue.

Brum's got the rope!

Suddenly, the rope snapped!

What are you going to do Brum?

11

The stone statue rocked and rolled across the Square.

Super-charged Brum **roared** after the runaway statue!

The stone statue wobbled and bobbled towards a big sheet of glass!

Tyres **thundering**
superhero Brum rolled onto the rope.
The trolley stopped.
But the statue
shot high into
the sky.

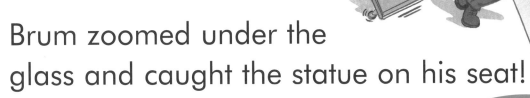

Brum zoomed under the
glass and caught the statue on his seat!

The Mayoress loved her new
statue. It looked super in
the Square.

"Hooray for Brum,"
everyone cheered.

Brum's
saved
the day!

Busy Big Town

Brum is whizzing around the Big Town. Can you see him?

Granny Slippers has lost her little kitten. Where is Lucky?

The Visiting Man is taking photos. Where is he?

The Traffic Policeman is busy today. Can you spot his horse called Arrow?

Bubble and Squeak are about to steal something sparkly from the Celebrity. Where are they?

Mrs Posh has lost her naughty dog. Can you find Scruffy?

mix and Match!

Whoops!

The Visiting Man isn't very good at taking photos. Put the two halves together to see who is mixed-up.

What is the Visiting Man's favourite game?

Snap!

16

Maze Muddle

Oh no! Granny has lost Lucky her little kitten. Mr Brillo can't find Gnorman, his favourite gnome, and the Celebrity's jewels are missing. Find the route to collect them all and return them to their owners.

What are you going to do Brum?

In the Shadows

It's a dark night in the Big Town. Naughty Penny Pincher has dropped some stolen things. Brum shines his headlights on them. Can you work out what she has pinched?

_ _ _ _ _

_ _ _ _ _

trophy

crown

watch

necklace

balloon

_ _ _ _ _ _

_ _ _ _ _ _ _

Look out!
There's a
baddy about.

_ _ _ _ _ _ _ _

Gnomes Galore!

Hoorah! Brum has rescued Mr Brillo's favourite gnome.
Well done Brum! How many spotty gnomes can you see?
How many stripy gnomes? Where is the Big Town Baddy?
Which is your favourite gnome?

Brum's a superstar!

What kind of rooms do gnomes like best?
Mushrooms.

Crack the Code

Oh no! The Big Town baddies are up to their tricks again!
They have stolen the safe from the bank. But what's inside the safe Brum?
Crack the code and help catch the baddies.

1 = a   6 = f   11 = k   16 = p   21 = u

2 = b   7 = g   12 = l   17 = q   22 = v

3 = c   8 = h   13 = m   18 = r   23 = w

4 = d   9 = i   14 = n   19 = s   24 = x

5 = e   10 = j   15 = o   20 = t   25 = y

26 = z

ANSWER: NECKLACE

Brum and the Big Town Balloons

 into the Big Town.

There were wobbly up and down and all over

the town.

Just then,  saw  buying a big bunch of .

Someone else was looking at them too.

Suddenly, the naughty grabbed the and sprinted

away.

Follow the Baddy Brum!

Superhero  zoomed after the .

The naughty stumbled across the Square and

disappeared!

Just then, a bunch of floated slowly out of

a in the ground. hurtled towards the hole,

flapping his doors and wiggling his wings.

The was stuck down the . He wouldn't be getting away.

All of a sudden, the floated away! Super-charged

 whooshed after the runaway

and scooped up the strings.

Superhero had saved the  !

Everyone clapped their favourite superstar superhero.

Key   Brum   Granny Slippers

Baddy   hole   balloons

Big Town Tangle!

Scruffy, the naughty dog, is causing mayhem in the Big Town Park. Mrs Posh is in a terrible tangle. Can you spot six differences between these two pictures?

Why did Granny Slippers put bananas on her feet?
Because she wanted a new pair of slippers.

ANSWERS: VISITING MAN'S TIE, SCRUFFY, WAVING MAN'S HEAD, LADY'S COAT, GRANNY SLIPPERS' HANDBAG, BRUM

Robbers on the Run

1

2

3

5 Slip on golf balls. Go back three spaces.

6

4

Swerve around the stalls. Whizz to 28. 24

23

22

25

26

27

30 Tumble over a gnome. Go back one space.

31

35 Bump into Mr Brillo. Have a rest.

29

32 Take a super short cut. Thunder to 34.

33

28

Where does a giant gnome sleep? Anywhere it wants to.

Nick and Rob are getting away with Mr Brillo's prize gnome. Throw your dice to thunder through the Big Town with Brum and capture the Big Town baddies.

Oh no! The gnome has gone!

9 10 11 12 13

...h a ...gnome. ...e forward ...spaces.

14 Stumble into a hole. Take a break.

19 Cross the road with the Traffic Policeman. Zoom to 22.

17 16 15

20 18

36 37 38

39 40 Cool! You've caught the baddies with Brum!

Big Town Balloons

Oh no! The Big Town Baddy has stolen some bobbly balloons. Motor through the maze with Brum and catch the crook in the middle.

After him Brum!

28

Big Town Quiz

Answer the crazy clues and fill in the grid.

Across

1. Who is the Big Town superhero?

3. Not goodies.

5. What is the name of the naughty dog?

Down

1. Who works with Job?

2. She likes to pinch things.

4. What is the name of Granny Slippers' kitten?

29

Brum the Soccer Hero

As Brum brummed by the soccer stadium something flew over the wall. Brum caught it on his back seat.

"Please can we have our ball back?" said the captain of the Yellow team.

Brum whooshed into the soccer stadium with the ball.

"It's one all," shouted the Yellow captain and he threw in the ball.

Come on Yellows!

Brum joggled and tooted as the Yellows raced down the pitch. The Yellow captain gave the ball a little flick and a big kick!

Now the Red captain had the ball. He ran to the Yellow goal and took a shot. The ball went into the net!

Brum rocked and revved. The Reds were not playing fair.

The reds are moving the goalposts!

Suddenly a Yellow player stumbled and tumbled. Brum zoomed across the grass and helped the player off the pitch.

Brum we need you!

"We need a new player," sighed the Yellow captain.

The Yellows cheered as super-charged Brum zoomed to the rescue.

No one saw what the Reds were doing down at the other end! They had rolled a sheet of plastic across their goal.

Brum whizzed down the wing, and nudged the ball to a Yellow player. He kicked it between the posts. But the ball **BOINGED** back!

Brum trapped the ball between his wheels and **thundered** towards the goal. Suddenly the Red captain grabbed hold of Brum's bumper. The referee blew his whistle.

It's a penalty!

Super-cool Brum blasted the ball past the goalkeeper.
It **smashed** through the plastic and went in the net.
It was the final whistle.

What a shot!

Superhero Brum had scored the winning goal! Everyone cheered their favourite superhero!

Brum's saved the day!

Lost Property

Granny Slippers, the Visiting Man, Scruffy and the Traffic Policeman are always losing things in the Big Town. Join Brum and look for the lost property. How many things can you find?

34

Spot the Difference

It's the Big Town soccer game.

These pictures are nearly the same, but there are ten differences. Can you spot them all?

Floury Footprints

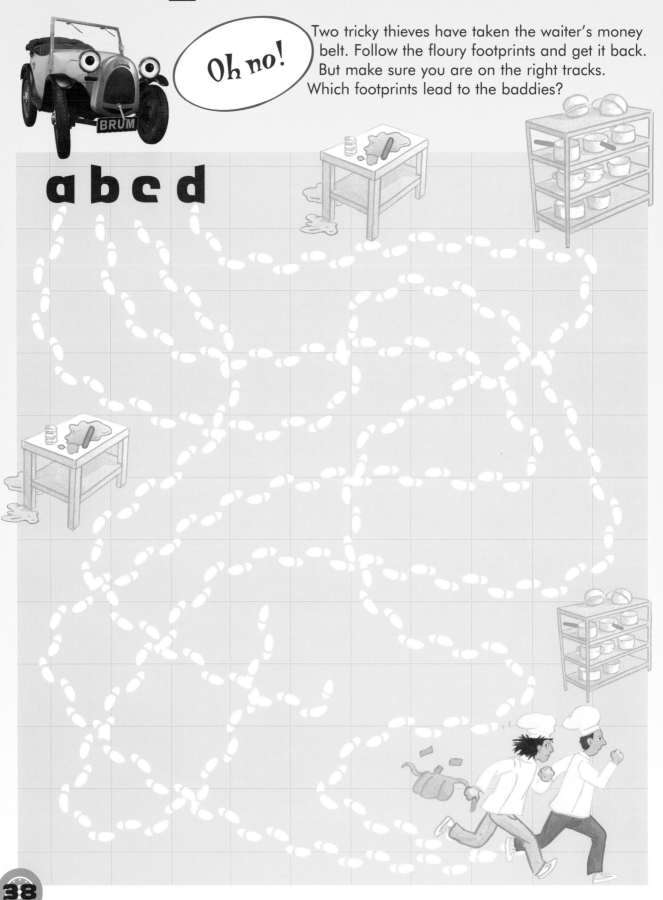

Oh no!

Two tricky thieves have taken the waiter's money belt. Follow the floury footprints and get it back. But make sure you are on the right tracks. Which footprints lead to the baddies?

a b c d

Airport Adventure

Bubble and Squeak are hiding in the Airport, but where?
Start at square one, move three squares to the right, five down,
and one to the right. Brum can see the baddies, but can you see Brum?

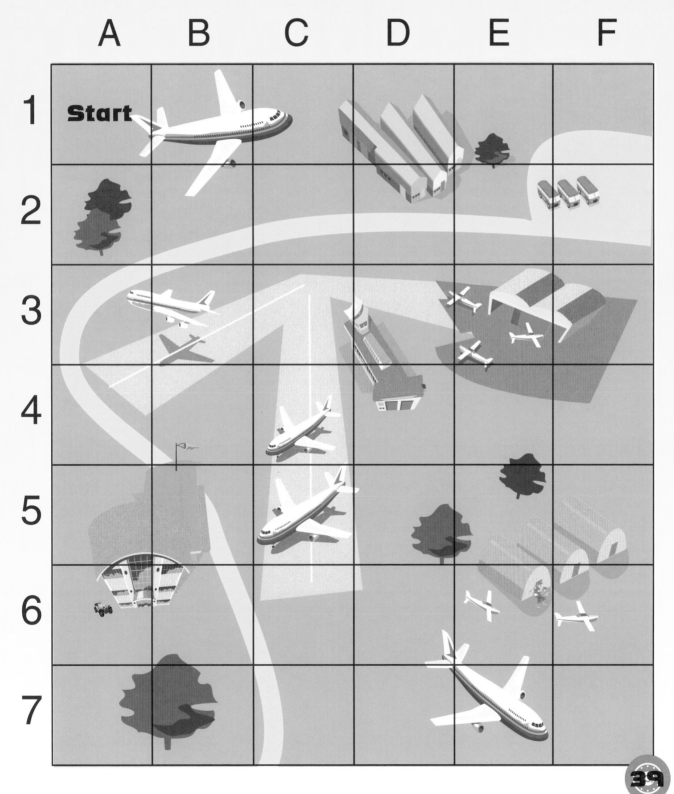

39

What's the Story?

The Visiting Man has dropped six photos. Can you help him put the pictures in the right order to show the story of Brum and the Super Stunt Bike?

What a muddle!

Brum and the Super Stunt Bike

1. Max Speed proudly shows Brum and Granny Slippers his shiny stunt bike.

2. Granny Slippers tries on Max Speed's helmet.

3. Suddenly the stunt bike shot off with Granny Slippers.

4. The stunt bike wobbled towards a very big ramp.

5. Brum nudged Granny Slippers onto a heap of hay.

6. Hooray! Brum's saved the day!

What would you call
Brum at the North Pole?
Exploring.
What would you call
Granny Slippers at the
North Pole?
Lost.

Where's the Golden Loo?

Bubble and Squeak have grabbed the gleaming golden loo and hidden it in the warehouse.

Can you spot it?

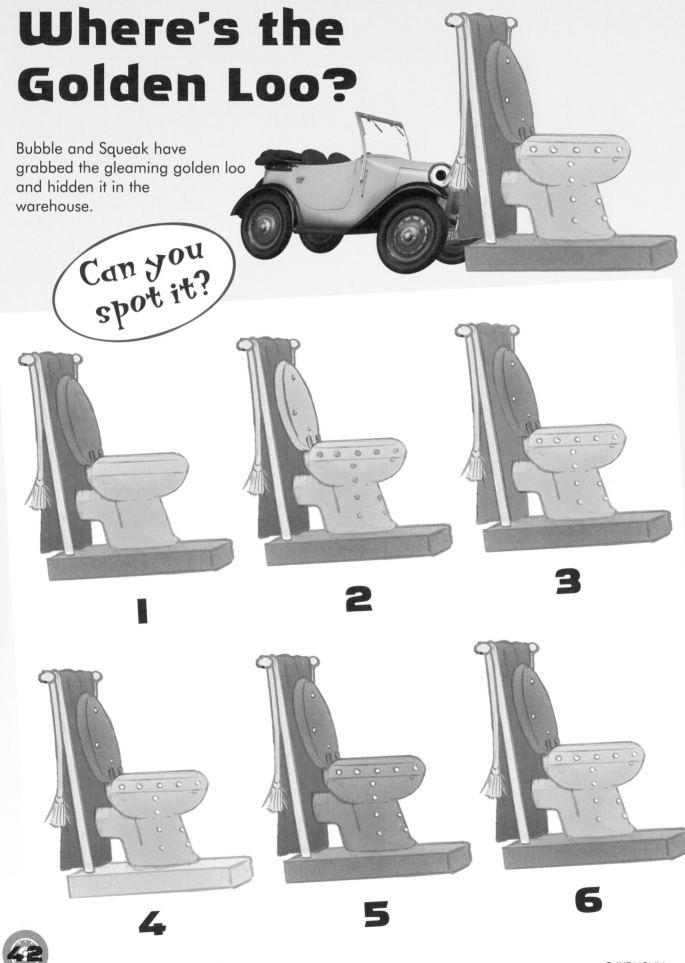

1

2

3

4

5

6

Kitten in a Tangle

Lucky the kitten has run away and got tangled up in a ball of wool. Help untangle Lucky by following the trails of wool. Which ball is she tangled up in?

Treasure Hunt

The Baddy is up to his tricks in the Big Town. Read the riddle below to find the first stolen object.

Carry on solving all the riddles until you have found all the stolen objects and caught the naughty Baddy.

'Opened up I make a sound and a dancer dances round. You can find me on the grassy ground.'

'I am round and float in the air, but you can find me in a Square.'

'I have no feet. I have a seat. You see me glitter like gold in the street.'

missing!

Brum we need you!

Mr Brillo has lost his favourite gnome. Mrs Posh can't find Scruffy. Bob is looking for Job and the Traffic Policeman is missing Arrow. Where are they Brum?

Draw a line from each person to their friend and save the day with Brum.

Who's Coming?

Here are four of Brum's Big Town friends. Name them all and then look at the letters in the red circles to work out who's in Town.

Who is in Town?

48

Floury Faces

Those crazy crooks, dressed as cooks, have been up to their tricks again. Everyone in the kitchen is covered in flour! Can you work out who is behind the flour?

Baddy Search

The baddies are on the run from super-brave Brum.
Find their names hidden in the wordsearch below and
save the day with Brum!

A	U	N	I	C	K
V	S	X	U	L	G
E	Q	C	E	O	P
B	U	B	B	L	E
O	E	S	S	P	N
R	A	N	I	Y	N
Y	K	R	O	B	Y

51

 and the music box

It was breakfast time
in the Big Town.

The Traffic Policeman
waved as Brum

whizzed by.

Arrow, his horse, was
munching a big red apple.

The Big Town ballet class was
about to begin! Two children were dancing
around a silver music box. Brum jiggled. Behind
the big sign someone was peeking.

It's time for ballet. The children twirled.

Brum whizzed his
wheels and whirled.
Penny Pincher crept to the
back of
the class.

It's Penny Pincher!

Suddenly she **sprang** forward...

...and snatched the silver music box.

Oh no!

Penny Pincher stumbled out into the street, and scrambled onto Arrow's back.

Brum **roared** into action and raced after Arrow.

But Penny **tippled**...

...and **toppled**...

...and nearly tumbled off!

Brum **thundered** through the Big Town.

What are you going to do Brum?

He backed into a market stall.

BUMP!

The apples tumbled onto Brum's seat.

Superhero Brum swerved past Arrow, swinging his door open.

All the apples rolled out.

Arrow's eating the apples!

Penny Pincher flew up into the air...

...and sploshed into the fountain.
SPLOSH!

The music box soared high
into the sky.

Brum whooshed forwards
and caught it on his back seat.

You're the
best Brum!

Brum **flapped** his doors and **wiggled** his wings.

"Hooray for Brum," everyone cheered.

Brum's
saved
the day!

Spot the Baddies

The bumbling baddies are back in town. But they can't hide from Brum forever!
Have fun with Brum and find the baddies and their stolen items before they get away.
How many can you find?

Scruffy's Lost

Oh no! Scruffy the naughty dog is lost in the Big Town Park. Follow the clues to find your way through the maze to find Scruffy.

Start

Finish

Tick-tock!

It's time to join the dots and find out who's stuck on the clock.

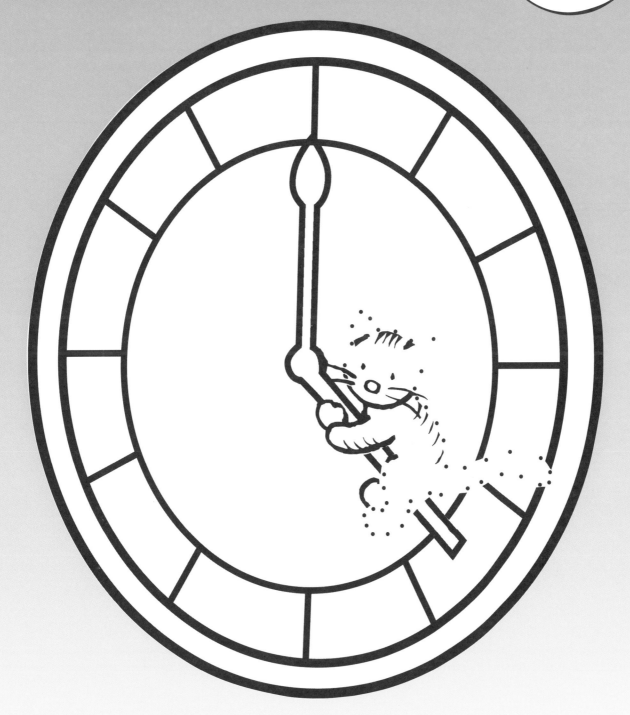

Where does Lucky do her shopping?

In a cat-alogue.

Here comes Brum!

Brum, Brum Gets Things Done

Brum, Brum, gets things done
A souped-up cruisin' superhero
Brum, Brum, here he comes
Brum, Brum, gets things done
A souped-up cruisin' superhero
Brum, Brum, here he comes,
Way to go Brum!

He's a supercar who'll always be
right there for you
Stopping things from getting away
A crazy superstar who's racing everywhere for yo
Brum's in town, saving the day

What sort of song do you sing in a car?

A cartoon.

Getting ready, wheels spinning round and round
Getting ready, revvin' to ride away
Getting moving, racing across the town
Brum's already on his way

Brum, Brum, gets things done
A souped-up cruisin' superhero
Brum, Brum, here he comes
Brum, Brum, gets things done
A souped-up cruisin' superhero
Brum, Brum, here he comes,
Way to go Brum!